SPOT THE DIFFERENCE

D0549307

SPOT THE DIFFERENCE

OVER 100 FANTASTIC PHOTOGRAPHIC PUZZLES

ARCTURUS

ARCTURUS

This edition published in 2012 by Arcturus Publishing Limited
26/27 Bickels Yard, 151–153 Bermondsey Street,
London SE1 3HA

Copyright © 2010 Arcturus Publishing Limited
Puzzles Copyright © 2010 Puzzle Press Ltd

All rights reserved. No part of this publication may be reproduced,
stored in a retrieval system, or transmitted, in any form or by any
means, electronic, mechanical, photocopying, recording or otherwise,
without prior written permission in accordance with the provisions of
the Copyright Act 1956 (as amended). Any person or persons who do
any unauthorised act in relation to this publication may be liable to
criminal prosecution and civil claims for damages.

ISBN: 978-1-84837-603-8
AD001531EN

Printed in Singapore

SPOT THE DIFFERENCE

Attention to detail is often said to be lacking in the modern, bustling world in which we live. Have you an eye for detail? Just how good will you prove to be at spotting when something is different? These pictures will test your powers of observation to the limit.

The puzzles range through five levels of observation, from Warm-Up to Expert, with the numbers of eyes indicating the difficulty levels: we reckon you'll need more than one pair for some of these intricate photos!

If you enjoy the stimulus of working against the clock, then we can give you target times:

⧗ Puzzles in the Warm-Up section should take no more than five minutes to solve

⧗ Standard puzzles should take anywhere between six to eight minutes

⧗ Challenging puzzles between seven and nine minutes

⧗ Tough puzzles about ten minutes

⧗ Expert puzzles may take ten to fifteen minutes each

If you can solve any of these puzzles in less time than recommended, then you really are observant.

In addition, there are puzzles which challenge you to spot just one difference, or to spot where things are hidden or missing; there are also reflected pictures, 'spot the same', negatives, and many other picture puzzles to provide variety, and to add to your puzzling pleasure.

Tick off the changes as you find them, then check to see if you are right, by turning to the solutions at the back of the book.

CONTENTS

EXAMPLE

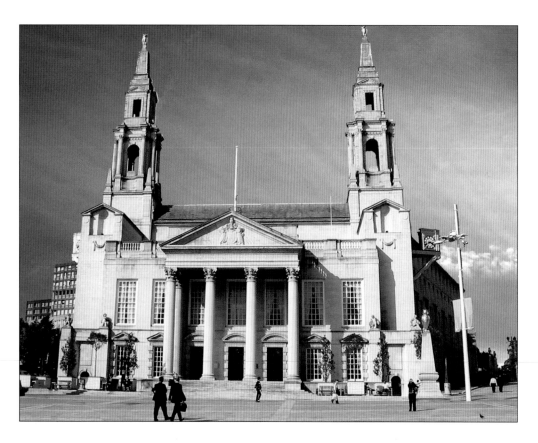

☑ ☑ ☑ ☑ ☑ ☑ ☑ ☑
1 2 3 4 5 6 7 8

PUZZLES

CHINESE FISHERMAN

1 2 3 4 5 6 7 8

CORKS

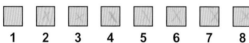

1   2   3   4   5   6   7   8

ONE DIFFERENCE EACH

3

★

1

1

1

1

SPOT THE ORNAMENTS

Of the six scenes below, which is the only one to appear in the picture above?

ORANGE BIKE

5

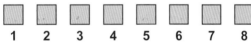

1 2 3 4 5 6 7 8

TROPICAL DRINKS

TROPICAL DRINKS

☐ ☐ ☐ ☐ ☐ ☐ ☐ ☐
1 2 3 4 5 6 7 8

ASTRONOMICAL CLOCK

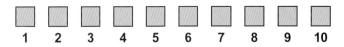

1 2 3 4 5 6 7 8 9 10

HAVING A GOOD TIME

8

1 2 3 4 5 6 7 8

BABY COOK

1 2 3 4 5 6 7 8

A MODERN HOUSE

10

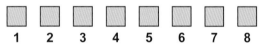

1 2 3 4 5 6 7 8

ON THE BEACH

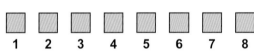

1   2   3   4   5   6   7   8

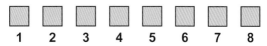

| 1 | 2 | 3 | 4 | 5 | 6 | 7 | 8 |

13 ORIENTAL GARDEN

ORIENTAL GARDEN

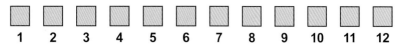

| 1 | 2 | 3 | 4 | 5 | 6 | 7 | 8 | 9 | 10 | 11 | 12 |

TROPICAL FRUIT

1 2 3 4 5 6 7 8

HIDDEN FISH

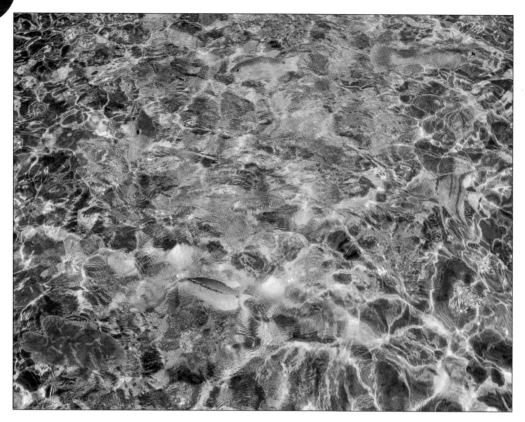

**The six fish below have all been hidden in the picture above.
Can you spot them hiding in the water?**

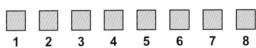

| 1 | 2 | 3 | 4 | 5 | 6 | 7 | 8 |

MARCHING BAND

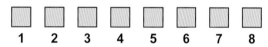

1 2 3 4 5 6 7 8

STRAW HATS

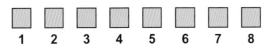

1 2 3 4 5 6 7 8

TOTEM POLE

1 2 3 4 5 6 7 8

DISCO LIGHTS

DISCO LIGHTS

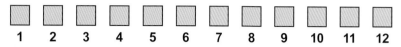

| 1 | 2 | 3 | 4 | 5 | 6 | 7 | 8 | 9 | 10 | 11 | 12 |

PAMPER YOURSELF

1   2   3   4   5   6   7   8

WRISTWATCH

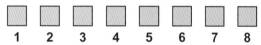

1 2 3 4 5 6 7 8

FIREWORKS

FIREWORKS

VEGETABLES

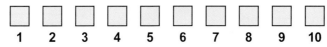

| 1 | 2 | 3 | 4 | 5 | 6 | 7 | 8 | 9 | 10 |

SNOWBOARDERS

1 2 3 4 5 6 7 8 9 10

KOREAN CARVINGS

| 1 | 2 | 3 | 4 | 5 | 6 | 7 | 8 |

CHEFS AT WORK

27

| 1 | 2 | 3 | 4 | 5 | 6 | 7 | 8 |

BIG WIGS

BIG WIGS

| 1 | 2 | 3 | 4 | 5 | 6 | 7 | 8 |

GLASS ANIMALS

GLASS ANIMALS

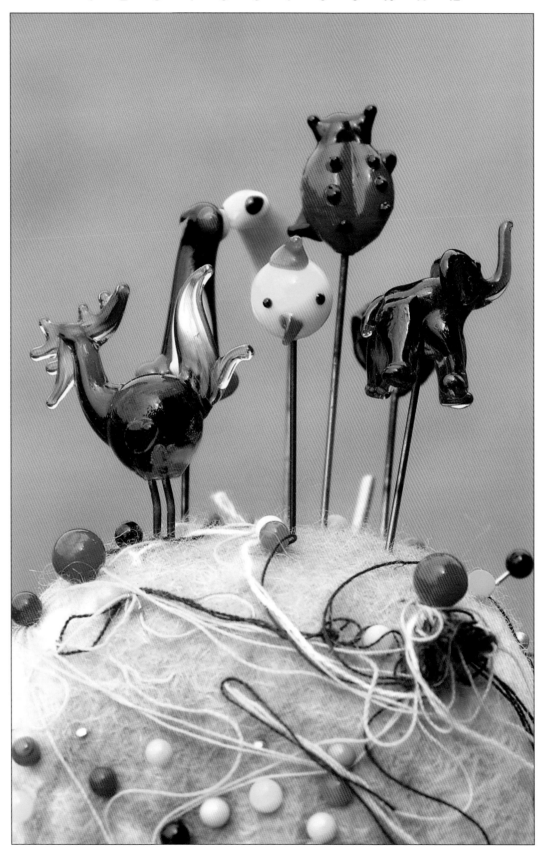

SHOES

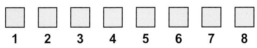

1 2 3 4 5 6 7 8

THE CAMEL

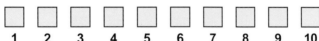

1	2	3	4	5	6	7	8	9	10

BROKEN TOYS

BROKEN TOYS

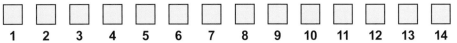

MANNEQUINS

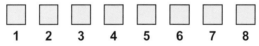

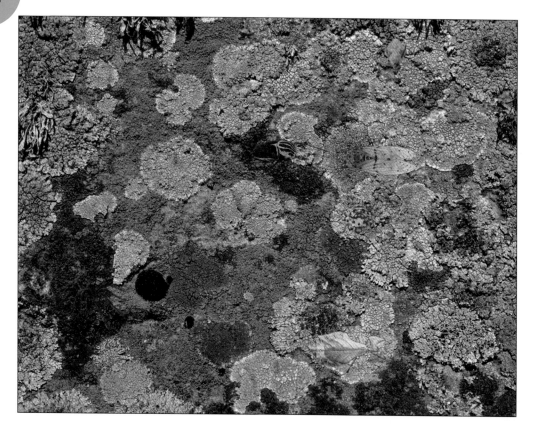

HIDDEN bugs

The six bugs below have all been hidden in the picture above.
Can you spot them hiding in the lichen?

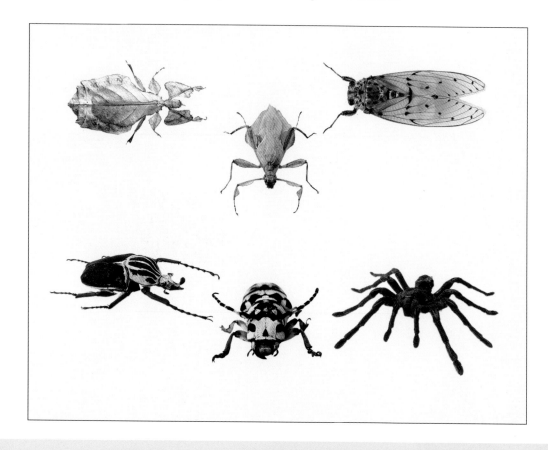

MASKS

MASKS

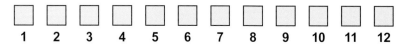

1 2 3 4 5 6 7 8 9 10 11 12

ALL DRESSED UP

ALL DRESSED UP

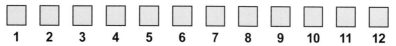

ENGINE PARTS

In which order should the twelve pictures above be placed,
in order to create an exact copy of the picture below?

SUNBATHERS

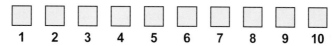

1   2   3   4   5   6   7   8   9   10

ONE DIFFERENCE

Can you spot the one difference in each of the four negatives?

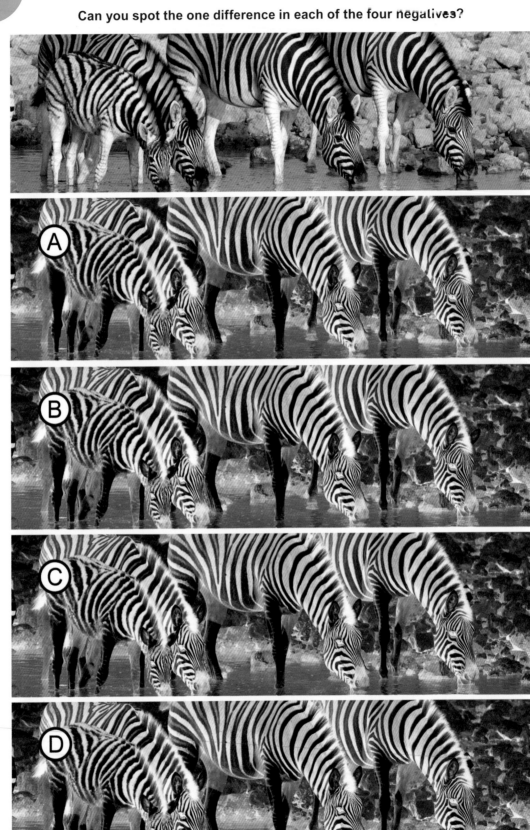

DOLLS' HEADS

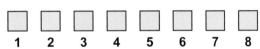

LAKESIDE

LAKESIDE

☐ ☐ ☐ ☐ ☐ ☐ ☐ ☐ ☐ ☐ ☐ ☐
1   2   3   4   5   6   7   8   9   10   11   12

MOSCOW OPERA HOUSE

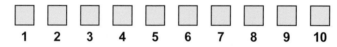

| 1 | 2 | 3 | 4 | 5 | 6 | 7 | 8 | 9 | 10 |

GEOGRAPHY LESSON

□ □ □ □ □ □ □ □
1 2 3 4 5 6 7 8

JIGSAW PUZZLE

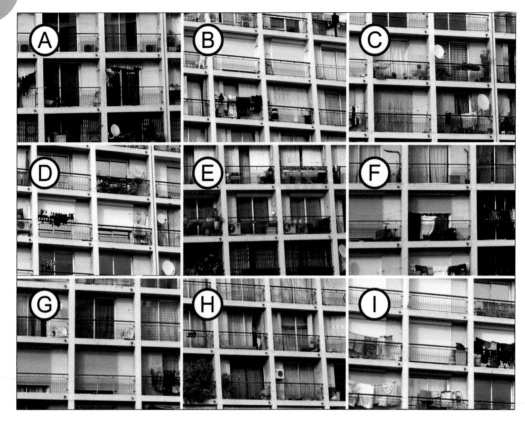

In which order should the nine pictures above be placed,
in order to create an exact copy of the picture below?

CLOTHES SHOP

1 2 3 4 5 6 7 8

HAPPY ARTISTS

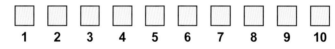

WATCHES

1 2 3 4 5 6 7 8

CHEESE SELECTION

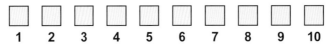

1 2 3 4 5 6 7 8 9 10

SPOT THE BEE

1

TRENDY LOFT

TRENDY LOFT

TRENDY LOFT

☐ ☐ ☐ ☐ ☐ ☐ ☐ ☐ ☐ ☐ ☐ ☐
1 2 3 4 5 6 7 8 9 10 11 12

WOODEN SHOES

WOODEN SHOES

☐ ☐ ☐ ☐ ☐ ☐ ☐ ☐ ☐ ☐ ☐ ☐
1   2   3   4   5   6   7   8   9   10   11   12

DIVING

SEAFOOD

| 1 | 2 | 3 | 4 | 5 | 6 | 7 | 8 |

CITY HALL

CITY HALL

☐ ☐ ☐ ☐ ☐ ☐ ☐ ☐ ☐ ☐ ☐ ☐
1 2 3 4 5 6 7 8 9 10 11 12

ONE DIFFERENCE

Can you spot the one difference in each of the five negatives?

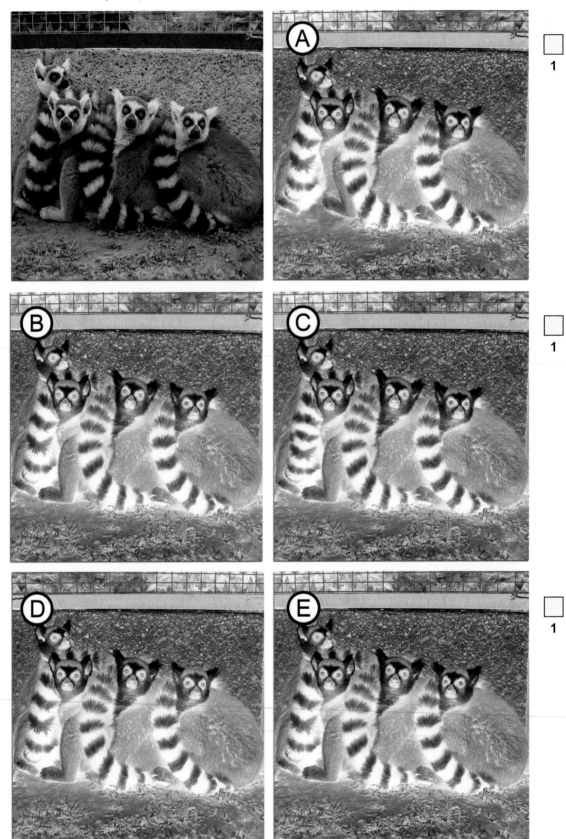

MACHU PICCHU

56

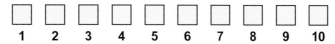

| 1 | 2 | 3 | 4 | 5 | 6 | 7 | 8 | 9 | 10 |

KITCHEN

| 1 | 2 | 3 | 4 | 5 | 6 | 7 | 8 | 9 | 10 |

BOWLS

1	2	3	4	5	6	7	8	9	10

CRUMBLY BUILDING

CRUMBLY BUILDING

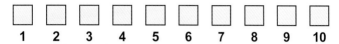

SEWING KIT

| 1 | 2 | 3 | 4 | 5 | 6 | 7 | 8 | 9 | 10 |

FUNFAIR

| 1 | 2 | 3 | 4 | 5 | 6 | 7 | 8 | 9 | 10 | 11 | 12 |

CUTTING OUT

CUTTING OUT

Of the six clips below, which is the only one to appear in the picture opposite?

THE CASTLE

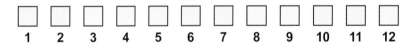

| 1 | 2 | 3 | 4 | 5 | 6 | 7 | 8 | 9 | 10 | 11 | 12 |

TIME FOR LUNCH

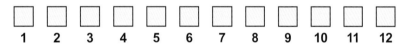

| | | | | | | | | | | | |
|1|2|3|4|5|6|7|8|9|10|11|12|

RUSSIAN DOLLS

1   2   3   4   5   6   7   8   9

TRAIN STATION

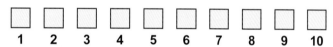

1 2 3 4 5 6 7 8 9 10

HENNAED HANDS

HENNAED HANDS

☐ ☐ ☐ ☐ ☐ ☐ ☐ ☐ ☐ ☐ ☐ ☐
1 2 3 4 5 6 7 8 9 10 11 12

HIEROGLYPHICS

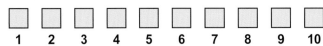

1   2   3   4   5   6   7   8   9   10

PANEL IN REFLECTION

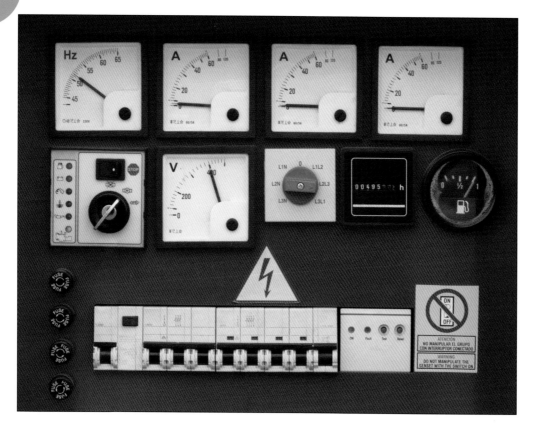

1 2 3 4 5 6 7 8

SHADOW PUPPETS

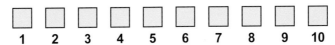

CHAMELEON

1 2 3 4 5 6 7 8 9 10

CHRISTMAS GIFTS

CHRISTMAS GIFTS

☐ ☐ ☐ ☐ ☐ ☐ ☐ ☐ ☐ ☐
1 2 3 4 5 6 7 8 9 10

WINDMILLS

WINDMILLS

☐ ☐ ☐ ☐ ☐ ☐ ☐ ☐ ☐ ☐
1   2   3   4   5   6   7   8   9   10

MESSY KITCHEN

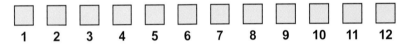

FRUIT

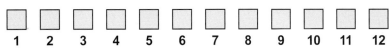

1 2 3 4 5 6 7 8 9 10 11 12

CHRISTMAS LIGHTS

CHRISTMAS LIGHTS

103

CLOTH ANIMALS

CLOTH ANIMALS

☐ ☐ ☐ ☐ ☐ ☐ ☐ ☐ ☐ ☐ ☐ ☐ ☐ ☐
1   2   3   4   5   6   7   8   9   10   11   12   13   14

JIGSAW PUZZLE

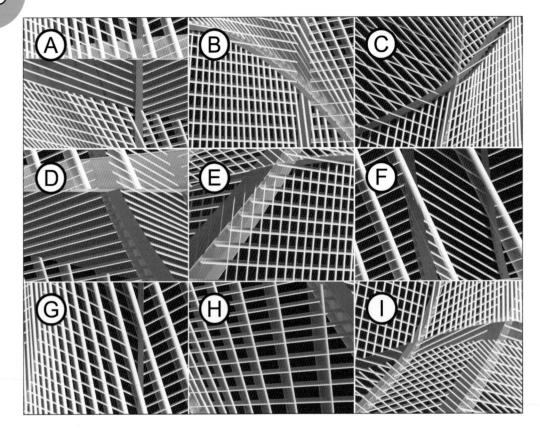

In which order should the twelve pictures above be placed,
in order to create an exact copy of the picture below?

HARBOUR SCENE

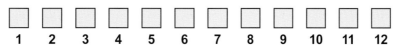

1 2 3 4 5 6 7 8 9 10 11 12

HOUSES ON A HILL

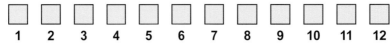

1   2   3   4   5   6   7   8   9   10   11   12

81

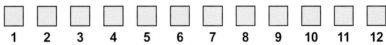

| 1 | 2 | 3 | 4 | 5 | 6 | 7 | 8 | 9 | 10 | 11 | 12 |

CUTTING OUT

CUTTING OUT

Of the six clips below, which is the only one to appear in the picture opposite?

VENETIAN MASKS

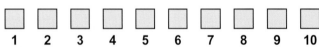

1   2   3   4   5   6   7   8   9   10

HOUSE CONSTRUCTION

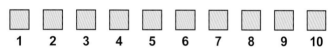

1 2 3 4 5 6 7 8 9 10

NATIVE SHIELDS

NATIVE SHIELDS

☐ ☐ ☐ ☐ ☐ ☐ ☐ ☐ ☐ ☐ ☐ ☐
1   2   3   4   5   6   7   8   9 10 11 12

STREET PROCESSION

STREET PROCESSION

☐ ☐ ☐ ☐ ☐ ☐ ☐ ☐ ☐ ☐ ☐ ☐
1 2 3 4 5 6 7 8 9 10 11 12

CIRCLES IN REFLECTION

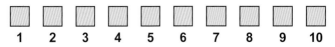

1   2   3   4   5   6   7   8   9   10

CHEMICAL PLANT

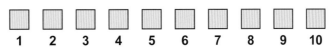

1 2 3 4 5 6 7 8 9 10

BOWLS

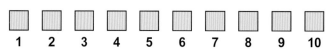

1   2   3   4   5   6   7   8   9   10

BREAD

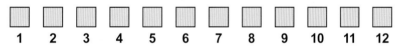

| 1 | 2 | 3 | 4 | 5 | 6 | 7 | 8 | 9 | 10 | 11 | 12 |

PAINTED CEILING

PAINTED CEILING

1   2   3   4   5   6   7   8   9   10   11   12   13   14

DRESS IN REFLECTION

DRESS IN REFLECTION

☐ ☐ ☐ ☐ ☐ ☐ ☐ ☐ ☐ ☐ ☐ ☐
1　2　3　4　5　6　7　8　9　10　11　12

TOTEM POLES

TOTEM POLES

ONE DIFFERENCE EACH

1

1

1

1

1

1

HAIRDRESSER

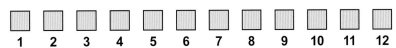

1   2   3   4   5   6   7   8   9   10   11   12

BEADS IN REFLECTION

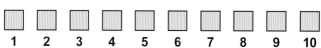

1   2   3   4   5   6   7   8   9   10

JAPANESE DOLLS

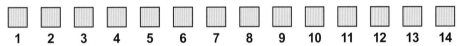

| 1 | 2 | 3 | 4 | 5 | 6 | 7 | 8 | 9 | 10 | 11 | 12 | 13 | 14 |

WALKING IN THE SNOW

WALKING IN THE SNOW

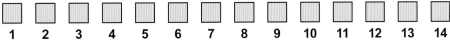

ISTANBUL

ISTANBUL

1   2   3   4   5   6   7   8   9   10   11   12   13   14   15   16

WEB IN REFLECTION

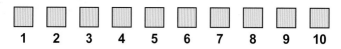

| 1 | 2 | 3 | 4 | 5 | 6 | 7 | 8 | 9 | 10 |

SOLUTIONS

1

2

3

4

5

6

7

8

9

10

11

12

13

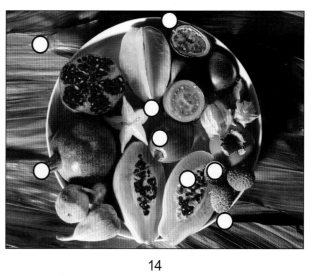

14

15

16

17

18

20

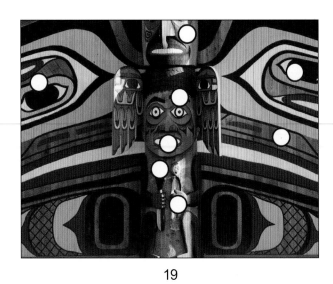

19

21

22

23

24

25

26

27

28

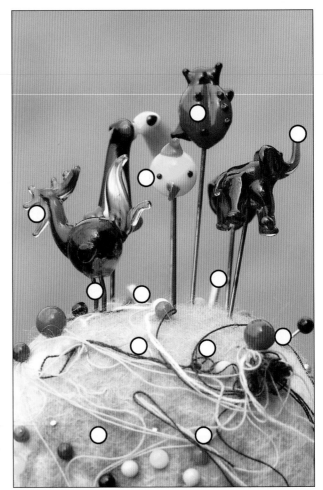

29

30

31

32

33

34

35

36

37

38

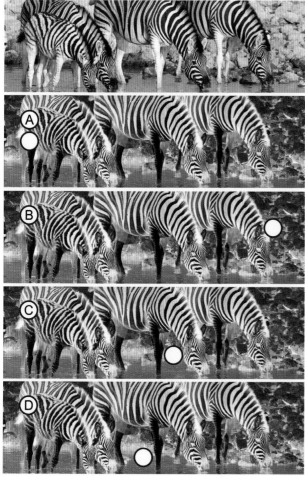

39

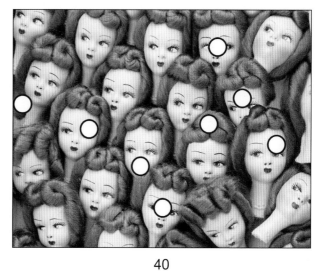

40

41

42

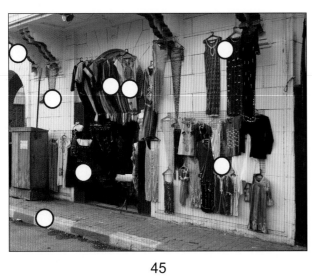

43

44

45

46

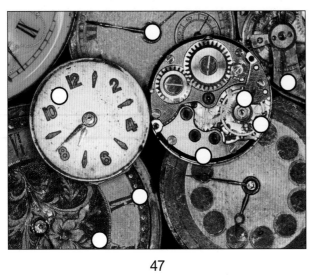

47

48

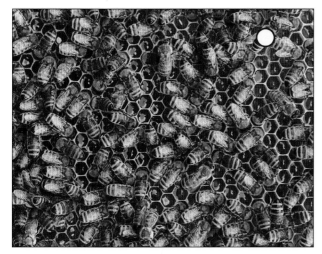

49

50

51

52

53

54

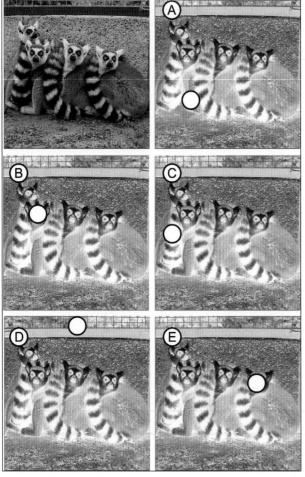

55

56

57

58

59

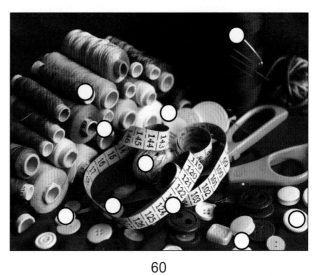

60

61

62

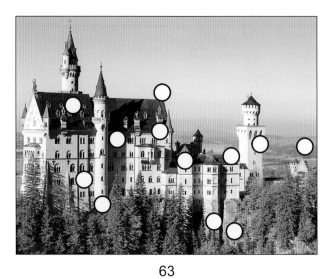

63

64

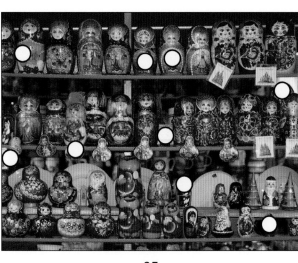

65

66

67

68

69

70

71

72

73

74

75

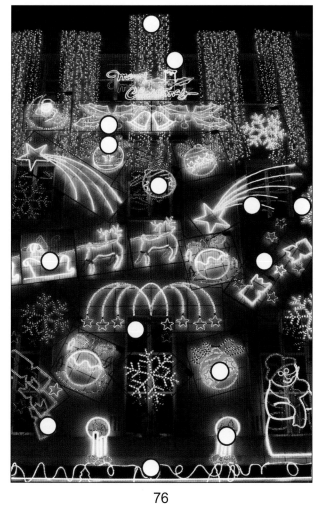

76

77

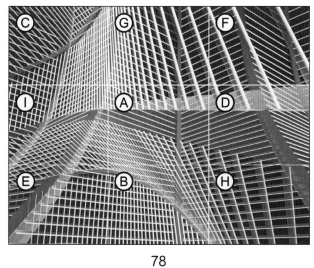

78

79

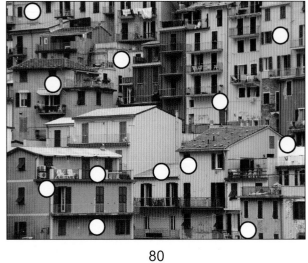

80

81

82

83

84

85

86

87

88

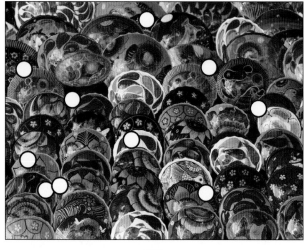

89

90

91

92

93

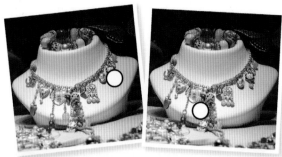

94

95

96

97

98

99

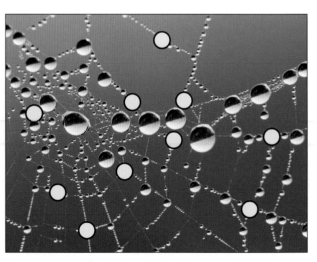

100